Written by Fiona Conboy —— Illustrated by Helen Smith

Edward the Unwanted Teddy

Edward was a beautiful teddy bear. He was bought as a very special Christmas present, but he'd been discarded in favour of a noisy new robot and a toy sports car. It wasn't Edward's fault but it seemed as if teddy bears weren't popular any more. He was soon abandoned in the toy cupboard.

Poor Edward was very shy and was too timid to talk to the other toys–before long nobody spoke to him at all. Edward didn't mind at first, but then he noticed that all the other toys were taken out to to be played with much more often than he was. Edward didn't understand why, but he couldn't find out because no-one would talk to him.

Every day Edward watched as the other more modern toys were pulled out of the cupboard. It didn't help matters that the noisy robot spent all day firing his guns. Then one day he heard a loud CRASH! The robot had broken into lots of little pieces and lay in a pile in the corner of the playroom. HOORAY! shouted all the other toys.

"Nobody liked the noisy robot," said Giraffe. "He wasn't any *fun.*"

The next day Edward and the other toys played together. Then the fairy doll piped up, "Does anyone know any good stories?" No one answered. "I'll bet Edward Bear does," laughed the Jack-in-the-Box. Edward blushed. "Well as a matter of a fact I do!" he said.

"Once upon a time ...."

At the end of the story everyone clapped. But the loudest applause came from the noisy robot. He had been mended and put back in the cupboard. "I never knew playtime could be so much fun," he cried. After that day Edward was never lonely again.

Lucy jumped into bed with her favourite teddy, Bernard, and gave him a great big hug to say good night. But something was wrong! Bernard always squeaked good night to Lucy, but tonight he didn't make a sound. He had lost his squeak!

"I must show you to Mummy in the morning," said Lucy to her bear. "She'll find your missing squeak."

Bernard slipped out of bed as soon as Lucy was asleep. He was going to find his missing squeak for himself. He thought he heard a squeak coming from the toy cupboard, but it was just Lucy's other toys talking in their sleep.

"I must find my squeak before morning," said Bernard as he squeezed through an open window and climbed down into the garden.

It was dark and Bernard was scared. Then he thought of Lucy and how much she missed his squeak. And as he trotted around the garden he trod on something hidden in the grass ... *SQUEAK!* it went. He bent down and picked up his lost squeak!

"My squeak!" cried Bernard. "It must have fallen out of my tummy, where the stitching was coming loose." He smiled, popped his squeak back and hurried back through the garden.

In the morning Lucy awoke and gave her Bernard a great big morning hug. *SQUEAK! SQUEAK!* went Teddy.

"You've found your lost squeak!" cried Lucy. All by yourself, too!"

"What a clever teddy you are!"

That afternoon, Lucy's Mum sewed Bernard's stitching up very carefully, so he would never ever lose his squeak again!

Teddy Boy Blue's New Outfit

Teddy Boy Blue was very proud of his new blue jumper and hat. The jumper had a lovely big yellow "W" on the front (although he didn't know exactly why) and the hat had a terrific fluffy yellow bobble on top. Teddy Boy Blue thought he was the smartest bear in the whole world. "I think I'll go and show everybody my new things," he said to himself, and then set off to go round the house.

He went into the playroom and found Sailor Sam tidying up his boat. "Have you seen my new outfit, Sam?" said Teddy Boy Blue proudly. "Isn't it lovely?" Before Sam had a chance to answer Teddy was off to find someone else.

"Teddy!" called out Sailor Sam, "you've caught your jumper on something!" But Teddy Boy Blue didn't hear him and went on walking.

In the hall he found Tabitha Dear with her friend Micky Monkey. “Hello Tabitha, hello Micky!” said Teddy. “What do you think of my new outfit?” But neither of his friends had a chance to say anything as off he went again. “Teddy!” said Tabitha, “I think you’d better come back ...”

Teddy Boy Blue went all over the house showing off his new blue jumper and hat, and then he met Jeremy Giraffe. “Hello Jeremy,” he said, “do you like my new hat and jumper?”

“I tried to tell you you’d got it caught on something,” said Sailor Sam, coming round the corner holding a big ball of blue wool, “but everywhere I went you’d just gone!”

going to rain."

"I think they must have got it wrong," said Fred, "the sun's shining and there's not a cloud in the sky–whatever the radio says, *I'm* going for a walk."

The pond was at the bottom of the garden, at the end of a long gravel path. By the time he got there he noticed there was a rather large black cloud in the sky. "Oooer," said Fred, as the first drop of rain fell, "maybe I should be getting back to the house." Half way up the path it began to pour, and by the time he got back inside he was completely soaked.

"Told you so," said Jemima when she saw Fred standing in the hall. "You aren't very fluffy any more, are you!" She was right, Fluffy Fred looked like he had just been swimming. "What am I going to do?" he wailed.

Jemima told him not to worry, and took him off to one of the bedrooms and got out a hair dryer; by the time she'd finished Fred wasn't only dry, he was even fluffier than he'd been before!

Wilbur's Snowman

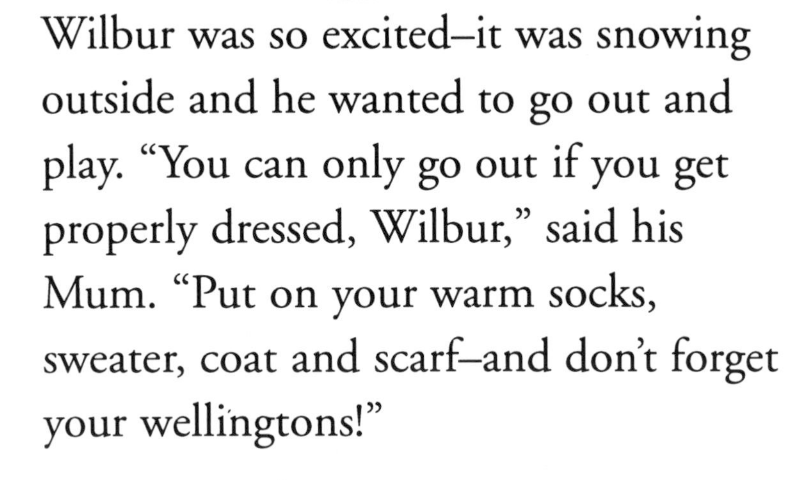

Wilbur was so excited–it was snowing outside and he wanted to go out and play. "You can only go out if you get properly dressed, Wilbur," said his Mum. "Put on your warm socks, sweater, coat and scarf–and don't forget your wellingtons!"

Wilbur couldn't wait to go outside and make a snowman with his friends. It was their favourite snowtime game. He put on his warm clothes and ventured out into the garden. "Be careful on the path, Wilbur" called his Mum. "Whoooah!" cried Wilbur as he skidded all the way along the garden path. "Too late!" he giggled. He picked himself up and made his way over to where his friends were playing.

"Look out!" called his brother. Wilbur turned around and SMACK! a big fluffy snowball landed on his nose. Wilbur and his friends fell about laughing.

There were giggles, and then roars of laughter from his friends.
"What did I say?" Wilbur asked.
Wilbur's brother asked him to close his eyes. He stood very still while his brother ran into the house to fetch their mother. Wilbur's Mum put a carrot on his nose and three pieces of coal on his coat.
"Surprise!" she cried. "*You're* the snowman today, Wilbur!"
All his friends had to agree that Wilbur was the best snowman they'd ever seen.

Next they all decided to play tag. Wilbur was chasing but he didn't manage to catch anyone as he spent all the time slipping in the snow and falling over! But he was having lots of fun. Until he ran BUMP! into the apple tree and WHOOSH! a large pile of snow landed THUMP! on his head.
"Isn't it time we started building a snowman?" asked Wilbur.

Terence's New Smile

Terence was not a happy little bear. He didn't look happy and, inside, he wasn't happy either. When Terence was made he'd been given a straight line for a mouth and no matter how hard he tried he couldn't smile–even when he was tickled.

"It's not fair!" said Terence. "I want to laugh and be jolly like everyone else, but I can't!"

When all the other toys were crying with laughter as they watched Jack the jack-in-a-box do his wonderful tricks, all Terence did was cry.

When everyone was playing funny games and giggling like mad, Terence didn't–not that he didn't want to, he simply *couldn't* do it. So he mostly ended up sulking in a corner which made him feel all the more unhappy.